C000101430

SUPER SMART
Times Tables Puzzles

ARCTURUS

ARCTURUS

This edition published in 2019 by Arcturus Publishing Limited
26/27 Bickels Yard, 151–153 Bermondsey Street,
London SE1 3HA

Written and project managed by: Penny Worms
Illustrated by: Graham Rich Design
Designed by: Graham Rich Design
Cover design by: Ms Mousepenny
Edited by: Kate Overy
Consultant: Amanda Rock

ISBN: 978-1-78950-303-6
CH006997NT
Supplier 33, Date 1119, Print Run 8056

Printed in China

CONTENTS

WHAT IS MULTIPLICATION?

I'm Dr. Whiskers and this is my family.

Multiplication is a fast and clever way to find the total quantity of something without having to count or add.

Counting and adding are perfect for when you have a small amount of something.

COUNT the mice...

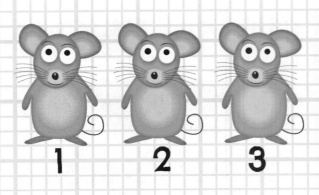

1   2   3

Three more mice arrive. You could count all the mice to find the total number, or you could ADD the two groups together.

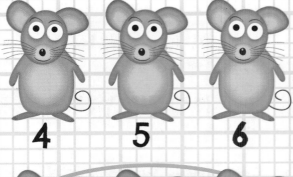

4   5   6

3 + 3 = 6

THERE'S MORE!

But what if another six mice come along. And then another six!
What have you got then?

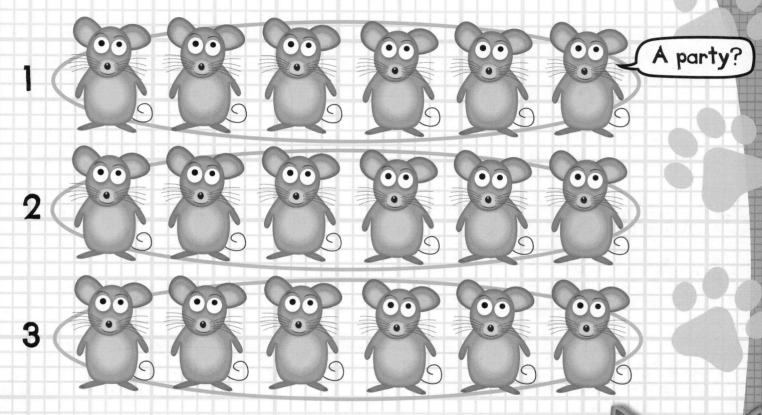

1

2

3

A party?

To find the total number of mice, you could COUNT them,
or ADD each group of six together, or you could MULTIPLY
them, because you have three groups of six mice.

3 x 6 = 18

And how do I know that 3 x 6 = 18? Because I know my
times tables, and you will too by the end of this book –
so just follow me, Sherlock Bones, dog detective.

WHY MULTIPLY?

Multiplication has lots of uses. Here are some...

MONEY

How much is the taxi?

We need 2 trips.

11 a trip.

11 × 2 = 22
That's 22.

PLAYING A GAME

You get 3 points when you score.

What's 3 × 3?

I have scored 3 times.

I have 9 points!

FINDING A QUANTITY

I have 5 mice coming for dinner. Can you buy me 12g of cheese for each mouse.

5 × 12 = 60
I need to buy 60g of cheese. Plus some for me!

TELLING THE TIME

If this is the time, how many minutes past 7 is it?

There are 5 minutes between each number, so 5 × 5 = 25.
It's 25 minutes past 7.

FINDING CLUES

There are different ways of saying 'multiply'.
To spot the clues telling you what to do, learn these terms.
Tick them when you can remember them.

Two **MULTIPLIED BY** three ☐

Two **TIMES** three ☐

Two **SETS OF** three ☐

The **PRODUCT** of two and three ☐

Two **GROUPS OF** three ☐

DOUBLE three ☐

2 x 3 ☐

THEY ALL MEAN THE SAME...

And the answer is **6**!

READY FOR MORE?

THE TIMES TABLES GRID

On the opposite page is a grid showing all the times tables together. You can see the numbers 1 to 12 in the yellow row at the top, and in the yellow column on the left.

If you want to find the answer to 8 x 9, trace your finger along the yellow row to 8 and then down the until you get to row 9. There is your answer 72.

Now find these answers.

9 x 8 = [ ]

6 x 3 = [ ]

12 x 11 = [ ]

7 x 1 = [ ]

10 x 6 = [ ]

12 x 2 = [ ]

Look at the numbers either side of the diagonal green line. They are mirror images of each other.

IMPORTANT MESSAGE FROM SHERLOCK BONES!

There isn't a 0 times table because all the answers are 0!

	1	2	3	4	5	6	7	8	9	10	11	12
1	1	2	3	4	5	6	7	8	9	10	11	12
2	2	4	6	8	10	12	14	16	18	20	22	24
3	3	6	9	12	15	18	21	24	27	30	33	36
4	4	8	12	16	20	24	28	32	36	40	44	48
5	5	10	15	20	25	30	35	40	45	50	55	60
6	6	12	18	24	30	36	42	48	54	60	66	72
7	7	14	21	28	35	42	49	56	63	70	77	84
8	8	16	24	32	40	48	56	64	72	80	88	96
9	9	18	27	36	45	54	63	72	81	90	99	108
10	10	20	30	40	50	60	70	80	90	100	110	120
11	11	22	33	44	55	66	77	88	99	110	121	132
12	12	24	36	48	60	72	84	96	108	120	132	144

All the answers are called MULTIPLES.
72 is a multiple of 8 and 9.

LET'S START WITH 2.

MULTIPLY BY 2

All the answers in the 2 times table are EVEN numbers, ending in 2, 4, 6, 8, or 0. The best way to learn them is to say them out loud, over and over again...

Using the table, or covering it up, answer these sums.

2 TIMES TABLE

$1 \times 2 = 2$
$2 \times 2 = 4$
$3 \times 2 = 6$
$4 \times 2 = 8$
$5 \times 2 = 10$
$6 \times 2 = 12$
$7 \times 2 = 14$
$8 \times 2 = 16$
$9 \times 2 = 18$
$10 \times 2 = 20$
$11 \times 2 = 22$
$12 \times 2 = 24$

$2 \times 2 =$ ◯

$5 \times 2 =$ ◯

$7 \times 2 =$ ◯

$10 \times 2 =$ ◯

$12 \times 2 =$ ◯

$1 \times 2 =$ ◯

When you times ANY number by 1 the number doesn't change.

PRACTICE TIME

Time to do some 2 times tables practice with Pip the Puffin.

Fill in the gaps in this number pattern.

2　◯　6　8　10　12　◯　16　18　20　22　◯

Now try it backward!

24　◯　20　18　16　14　◯　10　8　6　4　◯

Pip and his Pa have had a successful fishing trip. They have caught two lots of eight fish – eight yellow and eight blue. How many fish have they caught in total?

A CLEVER PAIR OF PUFFINS!

11

MULTIPLY BY 3

Remember, odd numbers end in 1, 3, 5, 7, 9. Even numbers end in 2, 4, 6, 8, 0.

Three is an odd number. If you multiply two odd numbers together, the answer is ODD. If you times an odd number by an even number, the answer is EVEN.

$1 \times 3 = 3$
odd × odd = odd

$2 \times 3 = 6$
even × odd = even

Using the table, or covering it up, answer these sums.

3 TIMES TABLE

$1 \times 3 = 3$
$2 \times 3 = 6$
$3 \times 3 = 9$
$4 \times 3 = 12$
$5 \times 3 = 15$
$6 \times 3 = 18$
$7 \times 3 = 21$
$8 \times 3 = 24$
$9 \times 3 = 27$
$10 \times 3 = 30$
$11 \times 3 = 33$
$12 \times 3 = 36$

$3 \times 3 = $ ◯

$8 \times 3 = $ ◯

$9 \times 3 = $ ◯

$12 \times 3 = $ ◯

Read out loud the answers in the 3 times table. Can you go beyond 12?

PRACTICE TIME

Look at these sums. Circle if the answers should be odd or even.

23 x 3 = | ODD | or | EVEN | 18 x 3 = | ODD | or | EVEN |

Flip the frog must jump from lily pad to lily pad in the order of the 3 times table. Help him by drawing arrows like the one below.

Flip can jump 3 puddles in one leap. How many leaps does he take to jump over 15 puddles?

YOU'RE MAKING GREAT MATHS LEAPS TOO!

MULTIPLY BY 4

Just like the 2 times table, all the answers in the 4 times table are EVEN numbers, ending in 2, 4, 6, 8 or 0. And if you look back, you'll see the answers are DOUBLE the 2 times table.

4 TIMES TABLE

$1 \times 4 = 4$
$2 \times 4 = 8$
$3 \times 4 = 12$
$4 \times 4 = 16$
$5 \times 4 = 20$
$6 \times 4 = 24$
$7 \times 4 = 28$
$8 \times 4 = 32$
$9 \times 4 = 36$
$10 \times 4 = 40$
$11 \times 4 = 44$
$12 \times 4 = 48$

Using the table, or covering it up, answer these sums.

$4 \times 4 =$ ◯ $11 \times 4 =$ ◯

$9 \times 4 =$ ◯ $2 \times 4 =$ ◯

$8 \times 4 =$ ◯ $5 \times 4 =$ ◯

PRACTICE TIME

Look at the table if you need to!

Help Pip with these sums.
Test yourself by covering up the table.

◯ x 4 = 28

◯ x 4 = 36

12 x 4 = ◯

10 x 4 = ◯

3 x 4 = ◯

Fill in the gaps in this number pattern.

4   8   ◯   16   20   24   ◯   32   36   40   ◯   48

Can you work out what number comes next? ☐

If you got the last one right, you know 13 x 4!

PIP. PIP HOORAY!

MULTIPLY BY 5

Odd numbers end in 1, 3, 5, 7, 9. Even numbers end in 2, 4, 6, 8, 0.

ALL the numbers in the 5 times table end in 0 or 5. If you multiply an EVEN number by 5, the answer ends in 0. If you multiply an ODD number by 5, the answer ends in 5. Easy-peasy!

Complete the sums below.

5 TIMES TABLE

$1 \times 5 = 5$
$2 \times 5 = 10$
$3 \times 5 = 15$
$4 \times 5 = 20$
$5 \times 5 = 25$
$6 \times 5 = 30$
$7 \times 5 = 35$
$8 \times 5 = 40$
$9 \times 5 = 45$
$10 \times 5 = 50$
$11 \times 5 = 55$
$12 \times 5 = 60$

$5 \times 5 =$

$3 \times 5 =$

$7 \times 5 =$

$9 \times 5 =$

$8 \times 5 =$

$4 \times 5 =$

Can you do this one?

$13 \times 5 =$

PRACTICE TIME

Now try these.

6 x 5 = ◯   2 x 5 = ◯   10 x 5 = ◯

◯ x 5 = 45   ◯ x 5 = 55   ◯ x 5 = 25

Clownfish love sea anemones. If Coco the clownfish visits five anemones a day, how many does she visit in a week? ☐

If Coco takes five minutes to swim round the coral reef, how long does it take her to swim round it three times? ☐

Complete this number pattern.

10 15 20 25 ☐ 35 40 ☐

Here's a tip! The 5 times table is half the 10 times table!

GREAT! YOU KNOW YOUR FIVE TIMES TABLE!

MULTIPLY BY 6

Look at the answers. The units go 6, 2, 8, 4, 0. This pattern doesn't change, so 13 x 6 ends in 8, 14 x 6 ends in 4...

There are two things to remember about the 6 times table. Because 6 is an even number, all the answers are EVEN. And they are DOUBLE the 3 times table!

Complete the sums below.

6 TIMES TABLE

$1 \times 6 = 6$
$2 \times 6 = 12$
$3 \times 6 = 18$
$4 \times 6 = 24$
$5 \times 6 = 30$
$6 \times 6 = 36$
$7 \times 6 = 42$
$8 \times 6 = 48$
$9 \times 6 = 54$
$10 \times 6 = 60$
$11 \times 6 = 66$
$12 \times 6 = 72$

$2 \times 6 = \bigcirc$

$4 \times 6 = \bigcirc$

$5 \times 6 = \bigcirc$

$11 \times 6 = \bigcirc$

See how 7 x 6 is double 7 x 3.

$7 \times 3 = \bigcirc$

$7 \times 3 = \bigcirc$

Write the above answers here.

Now add them.

$7 \times 6 = \bigcirc + \bigcirc = \square$

PRACTICE TIME

Now try these.

3 x 6 = ◯   8 x 6 = ◯   12 x 6 = ◯

◯ x 6 = 24   ◯ x 6 = 42   ◯ x 6 = 54

Flip eats six bugs for his dinner every day.
How many bugs does he eat in six days?

How many bugs does he eat in seven days?

Complete this number pattern.

6 ◯ 18 ◯ 30 ◯ 42 ◯

Remember,
6, 2, 8, 4, 0.

MULTIPLY BY 7

Time to sit up straight and concentrate! Ogor is about to show you the ogre's way to remember the two most difficult tables – 7s and 8s.

With multiplication it doesn't matter which way round the numbers go, so complete these sums.

You know most of your sevens already!

7 TIMES TABLE

1 x 7 = 7
2 x 7 = 14
3 x 7 = 21
4 x 7 = 28
5 x 7 = 35
6 x 7 = 42
7 x 7 = 49
8 x 7 = 56
9 x 7 = 63
10 x 7 = 70
11 x 7 = 77
12 x 7 = 84

7 x 2 = ◯   2 x 7 = ◯

7 x 3 = ◯   3 x 7 = ◯

7 x 4 = ◯   4 x 7 = ◯

7 x 5 = ◯   5 x 7 = ◯

Time to memorize the hard ones.
Complete these sums by COPYING from the times table.

6 x 7 = ◯   7 x 7 = ◯   8 x 7 = ◯

Now COVER UP the rest of the page, and complete the sums.
Say them out loud as you do them.

6 x 7 = ◯   7 x 7 = ◯   8 x 7 = ◯

Now complete this number pattern.

7 ◯ 21 28 ◯ 42 ◯ 56 63 ◯ 77 84

Jump 7 each time.
Use your ten skinny human
fingers if you need to.

MULTIPLY BY 8

Here's the best way to remember 8 x 8: 'I ate (8) and ate (8) till I was sick on the floor (64)!' Ha!

As 8 is an even number, you know that all the answers are EVEN. And also the 8 times table is DOUBLE the 4 times table. This could help you.

Complete these sums.

8 TIMES TABLE

1 x 8 = 8
2 x 8 = 16
3 x 8 = 24
4 x 8 = 32
5 x 8 = 40
6 x 8 = 48
7 x 8 = 56
8 x 8 = 64
9 x 8 = 72
10 x 8 = 80
11 x 8 = 88
12 x 8 = 96

5 x 8 = ◯

5 x EVEN ends in 0

2 x 8 = ◯

When multiplying by 9, the multiple starts with one less than the multiplier, and the digits add up to 9.

9 x 8 = ◯

8 is the multiplier

Now do these.

3 x 4 = ◯

3 x 4 = ◯

Write the above answers here.

Now add them.

3 x 8 = ◯ + ◯ = ◯

X8

Time to put it all into practice.
Cover up the times table and
complete these sums.

6 x 8 = ◯   7 x 8 = ◯   12 x 8 = ◯

◯ x 8 = 24   ◯ x 8 = 88   ◯ x 8 = 64

Now complete this number pattern by filling in the units.

| 8 | 16 | 2... | 3... | 4... | 4... | 5... | 6... | 7... | 8... |

Ogor has eight boots. Each boot has two holes. How many holes does he have?

If it costs, 8 ogre pennies to fix one boot. How much will it cost to fix all eight boots?

How much?!

MULTIPLY BY 9

Look at the answers below. The tens go up, 1, 2, 3, 4... The units go down, 9, 8, 7, 6...

Learning the 9 times table is simple if you know the tips and tricks – and there are many tips and tricks!

If you add together the digits in each answer (the product), they add up to 9.

9 TIMES TABLE

$1 \times 9 = 9$

$2 \times 9 = 18$

$3 \times 9 = 27$

$4 \times 9 = 36$

$5 \times 9 = 45$

$6 \times 9 = 54$

$7 \times 9 = 63$

$8 \times 9 = 72$

$9 \times 9 = 81$

$10 \times 9 = 90$

$11 \times 9 = 99$

$12 \times 9 = 108$

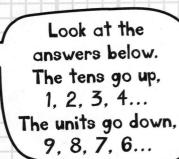

$7 \times 9 =$ **63** $6 + 3 = 9$

And from 1 to 10, the first digit of the multiple (the tens) is one less than the MULTIPLIER.

$7 \times 9 =$ **63**

7 is the multiplier. 63 is the multiple.

So, using these tricks, complete this sum.

$9 \times 9 =$ ⬤

PRACTICE TIME

Now cover up the times table and complete these sums.

3 x 9 = ◯   2 x 9 = ◯   11 x 9 = ◯

◯ x 9 = 90   ◯ x 9 = 9   ◯ x 9 = 54

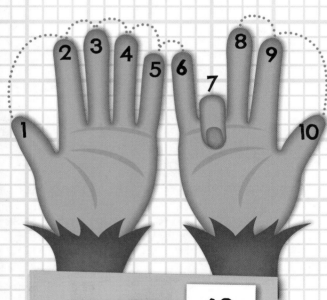

7 x 9 = 63

Use this method to do this sum.

Orla the orangutan is here to show you another magic way to do the 9 times table, using your 10 fingers. Imagine they are numbered 1 to 10. To times 7 by 9 (or 9 by 7) hold down the number 7 finger to reveal the answer.

The number of fingers to the left are the tens (6). The number of fingers to the right are the units (3).

4 x 9 = ☐

MULTIPLY BY 10

The 10 times table is easy to learn – even for Coco the clownfish (fish have very bad memories). Look at the answers. They are all the original number with a zero.

10 TIMES TABLE

$1 \times 10 = 10$
$2 \times 10 = 20$
$3 \times 10 = 30$
$4 \times 10 = 40$
$5 \times 10 = 50$
$6 \times 10 = 60$
$7 \times 10 = 70$
$8 \times 10 = 80$
$9 \times 10 = 90$
$10 \times 10 = 100$
$11 \times 10 = 110$
$12 \times 10 = 120$

Using the table, or covering it up, answer these sums.

$1 \times 10 = $

$8 \times 10 = $

$11 \times 10 = $

$2 \times 10 = $

$4 \times 10 = $

$7 \times 10 = $

Now try this one:

$13 \times 10 = $

x10

Time to some 10 times tables practice with Coco the clownfish.

◯ x 10 = 120

◯ x 10 = 60

Coco has collected 10 pearls every year for 5 years. How many pearls does she have? ☐

Fill in the gaps in this number pattern.

10 ◯ 30 ◯ 50 ◯ 70 ◯ 90 ◯ 110 ◯

Can you do this one?

100 110 120 ◯ 140 ◯ 160 ◯

The numbers go up in leaps of 10.

TIP-TOP TENS!

MULTIPLY BY 11

Look at the answers below. It's like seeing double!

The 11 times table is straightforward up to 10. So let's try those first. Look at the table and then cover it up.

11 TIMES TABLE

$1 \times 11 = 11$
$2 \times 11 = 22$
$3 \times 11 = 33$
$4 \times 11 = 44$
$5 \times 11 = 55$
$6 \times 11 = 66$
$7 \times 11 = 77$
$8 \times 11 = 88$
$9 \times 11 = 99$
$10 \times 11 = 110$
$11 \times 11 = 121$
$12 \times 11 = 132$

$9 \times 11 =$

$7 \times 11 =$

$6 \times 11 =$

$4 \times 11 =$

$3 \times 11 =$

$2 \times 11 =$

Now what's this one? Don't forget, you can switch the numbers round.

$10 \times 11 =$

x11

Now try these...

4 x 11 = ◯   3 x 11 = ◯   7 x 11 = ◯

◯ x 11 = 88   ◯ x 11 = 110

Complete this number pattern.

11 ☐ 33 ☐ 55 ☐ 77 ☐ 99 ☐

For 11 and 12, here's a tip. You know 10 x 11 = 110 and 1 x 11 = 11. So if you forget the answer to 11 x 11, add them together!

11 x 11 = 110 + 11 = 121

Using this method, work out 12 x 11.

10 x 11 = ☐

2 x 11 = ☐

12 x 11 = ☐ + ☐ = ☐

MULTIPLY BY 12

Look at the answers. It's 2, 4, 6, 8, 0 again!

These might be the biggest numbers in the times tables, but you know most of them already. Just switch them round.

12 TIMES TABLE

$1 \times 12 = 12$
$2 \times 12 = 24$
$3 \times 12 = 36$
$4 \times 12 = 48$
$5 \times 12 = 60$
$6 \times 12 = 72$
$7 \times 12 = 84$
$8 \times 12 = 96$
$9 \times 12 = 108$
$10 \times 12 = 120$
$11 \times 12 = 132$
$12 \times 12 = 144$

$12 \times 2 =$

$2 \times 12 =$

$12 \times 3 =$

$3 \times 12 =$

$12 \times 6 =$

$6 \times 12 =$

Now complete these sums.

$5 \times 12 =$

$10 \times 12 =$

$8 \times 12 =$

$9 \times 12 =$

x12

Cover up the table, and try these...

10 x 12 = [ ]   4 x 12 = [ ]   7 x 12 = [ ]

[ ] x 12 = 60   [ ] x 12 = 24   [ ] x 12 = 132

Complete these sums.

10 x 12 = [ ]

2 x 12 = [ ]

Add the answers together to find:

12 x 12 = [ ]

Doc the croc is 12 years old. When he is double that age, how old will be?

[ ]

When he is triple that age, how old will be?

[ ]

144 is the highest number in the times table grid. Do you know the smallest number? Have a look on page 9.

Both numbers only appear once.

ANSWERS

Page 8
9 x 8 = 72
6 x 3 = 18
12 x 11 = 132
7 x 1 = 7
10 x 6 = 60
12 x 2 = 24

Page 10
2 x 2 = 4   5 x 2 = 10
7 x 2 = 14   10 x 2 = 20
12 x 2 = 24   1 x 2 = 2

Page 11
The gaps are 4, 14, 24
and 22, 12, 2

Pip and his Pa have caught
8 x 2 = 16 fish

Page 12
3 x 3 = 9   8 x 3 = 24
9 x 3 = 27   12 x 3 = 36

Page 13
23 x 3 = ODD 18 x 3 = EVEN

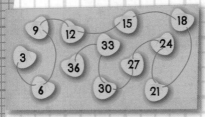

Flip takes 5 leaps to jump
over 15 puddles

Page 14
4 x 4 = 16   11 x 4 = 44
9 x 4 = 36   2 x 4 = 8
8 x 4 = 32   5 x 4 = 20

Page 15
7 x 4 = 28   9 x 4 = 36
12 x 4 = 48
10 x 4 = 40   3 x 4 = 12

The gaps are 12, 28, 44
52 comes after 48

Page 16
5 x 5 = 25   3 x 5 = 15
7 x 5 = 35   9 x 5 = 45
8 x 5 = 40   4 x 5 = 20
13 x 5 = 65

Page 17
6 x 5 = 30   2 x 5 = 10
10 x 5 = 50   9 x 5 = 45
11 x 5 = 55   5 x 5 = 25

Coco visits 5 x 7 = 35
anemones

Coco takes 5 x 3 = 15
minutes

The gaps are 30, 45

Page 18
2 x 6 = 12   4 x 6 = 24
5 x 6 = 30   11 x 6 = 66

7 x 3 = ㉑ 7 x 3 = ㉑
7 x 6 = ㉑ + ㉑ = 42

Page 19
3 x 6 = 18   8 x 6 = 48
12 x 6 = 72   4 x 6 = 24
7 x 6 = 42   9 x 6 = 54

In six days, Flip eats
6 x 6 = 36 bugs

In seven days, Flip eats
6 x 7 = 42 bugs

The gaps are 12, 24, 36, 48

Page 20
7 x 2 and 2 x 7 = 14
7 x 3 and 3 x 7 = 21
7 x 4 and 4 x 7 = 28
7 x 5 and 5 x 7 = 35

Page 21
6 x 7 = 42   7 x 7 = 49
8 x 7 = 56

The gaps are 14, 35, 49, 70

Page 22
5 x 8 = 40   2 x 8 = 16
9 x 8 = 72
3 x 4 = ⑫ 3 x 4 = ⑫
3 x 8 = ⑫ + ⑫ = 24

Page 23
6 x 8 = 48   7 x 8 = 56
12 x 8 = 96   3 x 8 = 24
11 x 8 = 88   8 x 8 = 64

The gaps are 24, 32, 40,
48, 56, 64, 72, 80

Ogor has 16 holes

He needs 64 ogre pennies

Page 24
9 x 9 = 81

Page 25
3 x 9 = 27   2 x 9 = 18
11 x 9 = 99   10 x 9 = 90
1 x 9 = 9   6 x 9 = 54

4 x 9 = 36

Page 26
1 x 10 = 10   8 x 10 = 80
11 x 10 = 110   2 x 10 = 20
4 x 10 = 40   7 x 10 = 70
          13 x 10 = 130

Page 27
12 x 10 = 120   6 x 10 = 60
Coco has 50 pearls
The gaps are 20, 40, 60,
80, 100, 120
and 130, 150, 170

Page 28
9 x 11 = 99   7 x 11 = 77
6 x 11 = 66   4 x 11 = 44
3 x 11 = 33   2 x 11 = 22
10 x 11 = 110

Page 29
4 x 11 = 44   3 x 11 = 33
7 x 11 = 77   8 x 11 = 88
10 x 11 = 110

The gaps are 22, 44, 66,
88, 110
10 x 11 = 110
2 x 11 = 22
12 x 11 = 110 + 22 = 132

Page 30
12 x 2 and 2 x 12 = 24
12 x 3 and 3 x 12 = 36
12 x 6 and 6 x 12 = 72
5 x 12 = 60   10 x 12 = 120
8 x 12 = 96   9 x 12 = 108

Page 31
10 x 12 = 120
4 x 12 = 48
7 x 12 = 84
5 x 12 = 60
2 x 12 = 24
11 x 12 = 132

10 x 12 = 120
2 x 12 = 24
12 x 12 = 144

Double (12 x 2): Doc will
be 24 years old
Triple (12 x 3): Doc will be
36 years old

The smallest number is 1